To
Stuart,
my celtic Prince
with all my love
Cathy x

THE
CELTIC
DAY BOOK

THE
CELTIC
DAY BOOK

A GODSFIELD BOOK

Library of Congress
Cataloging-in-Publication Data Available

10 9 8 7 6 5 4 3 2 1

Published in 1998 by Sterling Publishing Company, Inc.
387 Park Avenue South, New York, N.Y. 10016

© 1998 GODSFIELD PRESS

Distributed in Canada by Sterling Publishing
c/o Canadian Manda Group, One Atlantic Avenue, Suite 105
Toronto, Ontario, Canada M6K 3E7
Distributed in Australia by Capricorn Link (Australia) Pty Ltd
P O. Box 6651, Baulkham Hills, Business Centre, NSW 2153, Australia

Every effort has been made to ensure that all the information in this book is accurate.
However, due to differing conditions, tools, and individual skills, the publisher
cannot be responsible for any injuries, losses, and other damages which
may result from the use of the information in this book.

Printed and bound in Hong Kong

ISBN 0-8069-7054-5

Contents

January

BELIEFS

THE CELTS WERE A RELIGIOUS PEOPLE. EVEN JULIUS Caesar noted that "the Gauls are extremely superstitious." Their religion was strongly rooted in nature and they worshiped deities that personified the sky, the mountains, and rivers. Their spiritual rituals were an attempt to control or propitiate these forces, and some ceremonies centered on animal (or possibly sometimes human) sacrifices. For the Celts, demons were as real as angels, and for this reason, many of their prayers were protective charms. Many Celtic blessings abound, based on everyday tasks and rituals, from lighting the morning fire to tending cattle to preparing food.

The Celts held seasonal festivals, most famously Beltain to celebrate the arrival of summer and Samhain in winter, when the cattle were brought in from the pastures. As the centuries passed, the original pagan deities became merged with Christian saints. Brigid, for example, the goddess of wisdom and divination, was Christianized as St. Bridget.

JANUARY

1 Start of 2001, lets See what the year holds. Went to Bed 3.30 - 4.00 AM. Bad Start Argued.

2 ?!?! Made up for yesterday. What a Lazy day. Day off work sick!

3 Sarahs BIRTHDAY. Mum & Cath Met me In St ALBANS for Lunch. Things are good.

4 What a day! Paulo announced that he is to be Married in January Next year with me as Best man!! Great day at work, I will be doing training courses soon.

At this time the island of Britain was called Albion. It was uninhabited except for a few giants. It was, however, most attractive, because of the delightful situation of its various regions, its forests, and the great number of its rivers which teemed with fish; and it filled Brutus and his comrades with a great desire to live there . . . Brutus then called the island Britain, from his own name, and his companions he called Britons.

∽

**THE HISTORY OF
THE KINGS OF ENGLAND
GEOFFREY OF MONMOUTH**

*Three candles that illume
every darkness: truth,
nature, knowledge.*

∽

**ANON., TRIAD
9TH CENTURY**

10

THE SON OF
THE KING OF
SCOTLAND
BARGAINS WITH
THE GIANT TO
RELEASE THE
PRINCESS

Allies Fairy Tales

5

6 Helen over - Blind date with Jim.
Small arguement nothing much.
All really drunk when we got home.

7 *St. Brannoc, who established a church at Braunton at the place where he found a white sow and a litter of piglets*

Decorations down. Lots of tears
today. Cath unwell. Lots of
loving too.

I cannot sleep, I cannot leave
the house, I am distressed
because of it . . . After New
Year's Day, it is no lie, everyone
dresses in white fur; in the month
of January, the first of the series,
God makes us into hermits. God
has whitewashed the black earth
all around; there is no
underworld without its white
dress, there is no copse without
its coverlet.

**ATTRIB. DAFYDD AP GWILYM
14TH CENTURY**

JANUARY

HEAD OF A
CELTIC GODDESS
*Silver and gold
plated copper
plaque from the
Gundestrup Cup*

12

8 Meeting Shamilia (Paula's Bird)!
Couldn't go cath unwell.

9 Quiet day today
Cath feeling better.

Let he who is a chief
be a bridge.

~

FROM *BRANWEN*
DAUGHTER OF THE LIR
THE MABINOGION

10

Busy day at work.
I feel so close to cathnew

11

Quiet day today.

12 Work is going really well
at present, although its
early days yet.

13 St. Kentigern, the founder of Glasgow

Saw a serious wedding
dress for cathy today

14 Lazy day.
Mum has had 3 falls this week, 2 in house
and one outside. This is not normal for Mum.

13

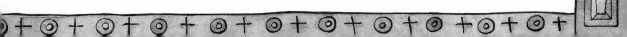

JANUARY

15 Start of week off.

Shopping WATFORD.

Car No ELECTRICS.

16 Lazy Day today.

A Feeling of Strangeness today.

17 Car Repaired today.

£100. Spent another Lazy day.

18 Paula over. went to poplars Nursery

Snowed

Paula Stayed over

. . . the man to whom open-handedness and bravery both come naturally may indeed find himself momentarily in need, but poverty will never harass him for long.

THE HISTORY OF THE KINGS OF ENGLAND
GEOFFREY OF MONMOUTH

Cold is the night in the Great Moor, the rain pours down, no trifle; a roar in which the clean wind rejoices howls over the sheltering wood.

ANON., IRISH
8TH/9TH CENTURIES

*Trees were objects
of reverence for the
Celtic peoples*

19 Went to oriental
World in Edware with
Paulo + Mum - Chinese for lunch - Brought PC Back in a shambles.

20 Went to Luton. Really Naff day. Didn't get
anything right much today - Snowed again
overnight.

21 Bad nights sleep. Irene + Steve over.
Day out to Hendon Museum. Brilliant.
Culths idea.

22 Back to work. What a shambles.
Cath coming down with a
head cold.

15

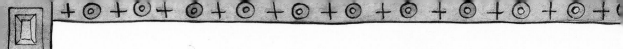

JANUARY

23 Busy day at work Cath not much better. really wet & windy.

24 Cath won £17 on Scratchcard. New desk + uniform for work.

25 Mrs Alexander married in Jamaica. Strange evening.

26 Day off. Awake all night.

They raised up music and
laid down woe;
There were soft drunken
draughts
And harsh stammering drinks,
Tranquil, easy toasts
Between himself and his
foster-brethren,
Music between fiddles, with
which would sleep
Wounded men and travailing
women
Withering away for ever;
with the sound of that music
Which was ever continuing
sweetly that night.

FROM *THE WARRIOR
OF THE RED SHIELD*

27 _____

_____

28 _____

_____

29 _Busy day at work_

_____

30 _Another Bad Day off._

_____

31 _____

17

Three smiles that are worse than griefs: the smile of snow melting, the smile of your wife when another man has been with her, the smile of a mastiff about to spring.

∾

ANON., TRIAD, 9TH CENTURY

He is stronger than any
laborer, more learned than
any druid, more acute
than any poet.

∾

FROM THE
WOOING OF EMER

_____

_____

FEBRUARY

IMBOLC

THE SEASON CELEBRATES THE EASING OF WINTER'S GRIP AND the optimism associated with spring. The Celts believed that the Irish goddess Brigid broke the Samhain spell of Cailleach, softening the hard earth with her white wand. She was worshiped as a seer and had three aspects as goddess of healing, smithcraft, and poetry. Brigid was one of the most important links between pagan and Christian beliefs, and became almost seamlessly associated with St. Brigid of Kildare.

Despite the birth of young lambs and calves, and thus the addition of dairy products to a spartan winter diet, Imbolc was not celebrated with great feasts such as those of Beltain and Samhain. Perhaps because of the connections with fertility and reproduction (nine months after the frolics of Beltain, Imbolc was associated with childbirth), it was regarded as a particularly feminine festival when women met to celebrate the arrival of spring.

FEBRUARY

1 *Imbolc/St. Brigid's Day*

I should like a great lake
of finest ale
For the King of Kings.
I should like a table of the
choicest food for the family
of heaven.
Let the ale be made from the
fruits of faith,
And the food be forgiving love.

∾

BRIGID'S FEAST
TRADITIONAL

2 Pay Day.

3

And they took the flowers of
the oak, and the flowers of the
broom, and the flowers of the
meadowsweet, and from those
they called forth the very fairest
and best endowed maiden that
mortal ever saw . . . and named
her Blodeuedd.

∾

FROM MATH, SON OF MATHONWY
THE MABINOGION

4

5 _____

_____

_____

6 _____

_____

_____

7 _____

_____

_____

8 _____

_____

_____

9 _____

_____

_____

BLODEUEDD
*Welsh goddess
of flowers*

21

*Never be greedy, always
be generous, if not in money,
then in spirit.*

∽

ST. COLUMBANUS

February

10 _____

_____

_____

*It is foolish for you . . . to rise
from quilt and feather bed; there
is much ice on every ford . . .*

∼

ANON., IRISH 11TH CENTURY
A CELTIC MISCELLANY

11 _____

_____

_____

12 _____

_____

_____

13 _____

_____

_____

CELTIC KNOT
DECORATION

14 _____

_____

_____

15 _____

_____

_____

16 _____

_____

_____

17 _____

_____

_____

18 _____

_____

_____

The royal roads were cow paths.
The queen mother hunkered on
a stool and played the harpstrings
of milk into a wooden pail.
With seasoned sticks the nobles
lorded it over the hindquarters
of cattle.

. . . And if my rights to it all
came only by their acclamation,
what was it worth?
I blew hot and cold.
They were two-faced and
accommodating.
And seed, breed, and generation
still they are holding on, every
bit as pious and exacting and
demeaned.

∾

THE FIRST KINGDOM
SEAMUS HEANEY, *STATION ISLAND*

FEBRUARY

19 _____

_____

_____

_____

20 _____

_____

_____

_____

21 _____

_____

_____

22 _____

_____

_____

"Welcome, father Ferghus," said Cú Chulainn; "if a fish swims into the rivers you shall have a salmon and a half; if a flock of birds comes to the plain, you shall have a wild goose and a half; a handful of water-cress or dulse, a handful of brook-lime, and a drink from the sand. If it happens to be your watch, you shall have someone to go to the ford to meet all comers, so that you may go to sleep."

∽

FROM *THE KILLING OF EDARCOMHOL*

Raw and cold is icy spring . . . birds awaken from meadows, many are the wild creatures from which they flee out of the wood, out of the green grass . . .

∽

ANON.

23 _____

_____

24 _____

_____

25 _____

_____

26 _____

_____

27 _____

FERGUS AND
THE WEE MAN

_____

28 _____

_____

29 _____

_____

*For it is the prince's falsehood
that brings perverse weather
upon wicked peoples and dries
up the fruits of the earth.*

∾

ANON.
TRANS. CAITLÍN MATTHEWS

_____

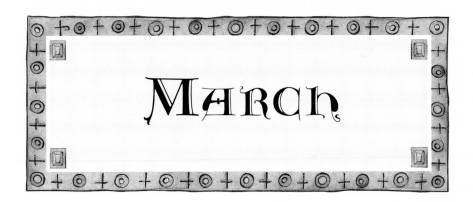

MARCH

LEGENDS

ALL CELTIC KNOWLEDGE WAS TRANSMITTED ORALLY, and "the joint memory of the seniors" helped preserve a respect for the older members of society as repositories of wisdom. The Celts left virtually no written records apart from a few inscribed headstones and basic trading records; they had no written literary tradition. The first Celtic myths were written down in the 8th century by Christian monks, and there is no doubt that many of the ancient tales (possibly already a thousand years old) were dramatically altered, although they incorporated elements of the original pagan Celtic stories.

Their myths recount stories of the gods, tell heroic tales of battles, and explain the history of the people, the Irish myths in particular recounting many invasions. All the tales revel in the powerful forces of nature and the unknown. Certain themes persist – the magical powers of water, caldrons, and the belief in the sacred power of the head as the center of the soul.

MARCh

1 *St. David's Day*

_____

_____

_____

2 _____

_____

_____

A hedge before me, one behind,
a blackbird sings from that,
above my small book many-lined
I apprehend his chat.

Up trees, in costumes buff,
mild accurate cuckoos bleat,
Lord love me, good the stuff
I write in a shady seat.

∾

FROM *THE MONASTIC SCRIBE*
ANON., 9TH CENTURY

3 _____

_____

_____

4 _____

_____

_____

. . . Arthur's sword in his hand,
and the image of two serpents on
the sword in gold; and when the
sword was drawn from its sheath
. . . two flames of fire might be
seen from the mouths of the
serpents, and so exceeding
dreadful was it that it was not
easy for any to look thereon.

∾

FROM *THE DREAM OF RHONABWY*
THE MABINOGION

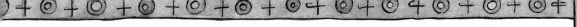

5

6 *Festival of the goddess Eriu, whose name – as Eire – was given to the island of Ireland*

7

> *May we keep faith or let the
> sky fall and crush us, the earth
> open up and swallow us, or the
> sea rise up and overwhelm us.*
>
> ❧
>
> **ANCIENT CELTIC OATH
> TRANS. CAITLÍN MATTHEWS**

MARCH

EMER REBUKED
BY CÚ CHULAINN

30

8

_____

_____

_____

9

_____

_____

I made my song a coat
Covered with embroideries
Out of old mythologies

❧

FROM *A COAT*
W. B. YEATS

10 _____

_____

_____

11 _____

_____

_____

12 _____

_____

13 _____

_____

_____

14 _____

_____

_____

Three slender things that best support the world: the slender stream of milk from the cow's dug into the pail; the slender blade of green corn upon the ground; the slender thread over the hand of a skilled woman.

ANON., TRIAD, 9TH CENTURY

Cú Chulainn slept with Fann, and he abode for a month in her company, and at the end of the month he came to bid her farewell. "Tell me," she said, "to what place I may go for our tryst, and I will be there." . . . Now word was brought to Emer of that tryst, and knives were whetted by Emer to slay the fairy woman . . .

FROM *THE WASTING SICKNESS OF CÚ CHULAINN*

MARCH

15 _____

_____

_____

16 _____

_____

_____

32

17 *St. Patrick's Day* _____

_____

_____

18 _____

_____

_____

God's shield to protect me,
God's legions to save me
from snares of the demons
from evil enticements
from failings of nature
from one man or many
that seek to destroy me
anear or from far.

ST. PATRICK'S BREASTPLATE

The women of Ulster loved
Cú Chulainn for his dexterity in
the feats, for the nimbleness of
his leap, for the excellence of his
wisdom, for the sweetness of his
speech, for the beauty of his face,
for the loveliness of his look.

FROM *THE WOOING OF EMER*

CÚ CHULAINN
RIDES A CELTIC
WAR CHARIOT

19

20

21 *Alban Eiler (Light of the Earth) Spring Equinox*

22

*Be submissive to good,
unbending to evil, gentle in
curiosity, untiring in love,
just in all things . . .*

∽

ST. COLUMBANUS

MARCH

23 _____

_____

Power of eye upon you,
Power of the elements upon you,
Power of my heart's wish.

∾

TRADITIONAL
TRANS. CAITLÍN MATTHEWS

24 _____

_____

_____

25 *Lady Day, dedicated of old to the Virgin Mary* _____

_____

26 _____

_____

_____

THE EIGHT
CIRCLE CROSS
Book of Kells

27 _____

_____

_____

28 _____

_____

_____

29 _____

_____

30 _____

_____

_____

31 _Slipped Disc operation 2014._

_____

_____

In Ireland, meanwhile, there was not a man left alive, only five pregnant women in a cave in the wilderness, and these women all bore sons at the same moment. The boys were reared until they grew into big lads; their thoughts turned to women and they desired to take wives, so each one in turn slept with his companions' mothers. They lived in the land and ruled it and divided it among the five of them, and because of that division the five parts of Ireland are still called fifths.

∾

FROM *BRANWEN, DAUGHTER OF LIR*
THE MABINOGION

I have been brought up . . . among poets and learned men, among the lords of land and farmers of Ulster have I been reared, so that I have all their manners and gifts.

∾

FROM *THE WOOING OF EMER*

April

WAR AND WARRIORS

The myths of *The Mabinogion* and Ireland are full of larger-than-life warriors, who exhibit outstanding bravery, and demonstrate tremendous feats of valor and strength. The Celts, for all their love of display and fine jewelry, clearly loved a bloodthirsty tale, but such stories may simply have been an exaggerated reflection of their fighting habits.

In many tales, warriors cut off their enemies' heads, partly because they believed that the killer would be endowed with the dead man's energy. The legendary giant Bran ordered that his own head be placed in the White Tower in London, where it would protect Britain. As Gerald of Wales remarked, families bore grudges, remembering and avenging insults for generations. Julius Caesar, who fought more than his fair share of Celtic warriors, respected them. "The ancient Britons . . . dye themselves blue with woad, so that they seem more terrifying in battle."

APRIL

1 _____

_____

_____

2 _____

_____

38

_____

3 _____

_____

_____

4 _____

_____

THE WASHER
AT THE FORD
*Washing away
the blood of a
fallen warrior*

_____

5 _____

_____

_____

_____

6 _____

_____

_____

_____

7 _____

_____

A lesson which they take particular pains to inculcate is that the soul does not perish, but after death passes from one body to another; they think that this is the best incentive to bravery, because it teaches men to disregard the terrors of death.

∽

THE CONQUEST OF GAUL
JULIUS CAESAR

. . . time was a backward rote of names and mishaps, bad harvests, fires, unfair settlements, deaths in floods, murders, and miscarriages.

∽

FROM *THE FIRST KINGDOM*
SEAMUS HEANEY

_____

_____

Empty the country where there is no religion The unbeliever does not think of God

∽

THE VIATICUM OF
LLEFOED WYNEBGLAWR
TRANS. CAITLÍN MATTHEWS

April

8 _____

_____

_____

*On the eighth of
the calends of April
Flights of swallows make
congregation . . .*

∾

THE BOOK OF LEINSTER
TRANS. CAITLÍN MATTHEWS

9 _____

_____

_____

THE
THREE
FATES

10 _____

_____

_____

11 _____

_____

_____

12 _____

_____

_____

13 _____

_____

_____

14 _____

_____

_____

As long as a weaver's beam was each of her two shins, and they were as dark as the back of a stag-beetle. A grayish woolly mantle she wore. Her lower hair reached as far as her knee. Her lips were on one side of her head. She came and put one of her shoulders against the doorpost of the house, casting the evil eye on the king.

❧

THE GODDESS BADBH APPEARS TO KING CONAIRE TO PROPHESY HIS DEATH

The three with the lightest hearts: a student reading his psalms, a young lad who has left off his boy's clothes for good, a maid who has been made a woman.

❧

ANON., TRIAD, 9TH CENTURY

April

15

_____

_____

_____

16

_____

_____

_____

17

_____

_____

_____

18

_____

_____

_____

_____

. . . King of the Tree of Life with its flowers, the space around which noble hosts were ranged, its crest, and its showers on every side spread over the fields and plains of Heaven.

On it sits a glorious flock of birds and sings perfect songs of purest grace; without withering (with choice bounty rather) of fruit and leaves.

Lovely is the flock of birds which keeps it, on every bright and goodly bird a hundred feathers; and without sin, with pure brilliance, they sing a hundred tunes for every feather . . .

∽

FROM _THE TREE OF LIFE_

A CELTIC
WARRIOR AND
HIS HOUND

19 _____

_____

_____

20 _____

_____

21 _____

_____

22 _____

_____

He was too young . . .
too daring . . .
and too beautiful.

∽

FROM THE
WOOING OF EMER

_____

April

23 _____

_____

_____

24 _____

_____

_____

And from that time forth they began to make strong the bond of friendship between them, and each sent to the other horses and grayhounds and hawks and all such treasures as they thought would be pleasing to the heart of either.

ॐ

FROM *PWYLL, PRINCE OF DYFED*
THE MABINOGION

25 _____

_____

_____

26 _____

_____

_____

Be . . . unshaken in turmoil,
valiant in the cause of truth,
cautious in time of strife.

ॐ

ST. COLUMBANUS

27 _____

_____

_____

28 _____

_____

29 _____

_____

_____

30 *Beltain Eve – fires were rekindled* _____

_____

_____

In spring the land is partly bare,
If people are turbulent, their
shout is deceitful.
In calm reflection riches are
despised.
What is not often seen is
neglected.

~

*THE VIATICUM OF LLEFOED
WYNEBGLAWR*
TRANS. CAITLÍN MATTHEWS

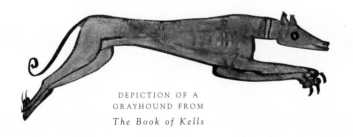

DEPICTION OF A
GRAYHOUND FROM
The Book of Kells

MAY

BELTAIN

BELTAIN AND SAMHAIN WERE THE TWO GREATEST FESTIVALS in the Celtic year. Beltain celebrated the season of growth, when Celtic farmers followed their herds to the higher pastures for summer grazing. It marked the start of summer, when the trees were in bud and colorful flowers peppered the landscape. With the arrival of warmer weather, tribes traveled to exchange news with their neighbors, and fairs were held. It was also the traditional time for feuding and warfare to begin. The roving troops of Fionn Mac Cumhail lived off the land from Beltain until Samhain, and for the rest of the year were supported during the colder months by the people in winter quarters.

Details of Beltain rituals are sketchy, but the word incorporates the word *teine*, or fire, and great fires were important, partly used to purge winter diseases. Lighting the Beltain fire was an honor reserved for druids, and the rest of the festival was associated with courting, as young couples traditionally went into the woods on Beltain eve. With a great deal of dancing, singing, and merriment, it is the ancestor of May Day celebrations.

MAY

1   *Beltain*

2

3

4

Everything within my dwellings
or in my possession,
All line and crops, all flock
and corn.

〜

FROM *HALLOW EVE TO BELTAIN EVE*
BELTAIN BLESSING

...When on a summer morning
early the curly-haired chief arises
for the deer-hunt, there is dew
on the grass, the blackbird
warbling, and the life has gone
out of the frost.

〜

*THE FERTILE LANDS
OF CATHAL Ó CONCHOBAIR*
GIOLLA BRIGHDE MACCONMIDHE
13TH CENTURY

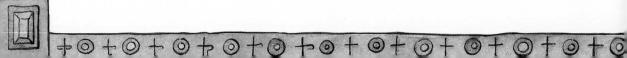

GUINEVERE PICKS
MAY BLOSSOM

5 _____

_____

_____

6 _____

_____

_____

7 _____

_____

_____

May-time, fairest season,
noisy are the birds,
green the woods, the plows
are in the furrow . . .

∽

ANON., WELSH
12TH CENTURY

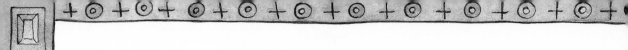

May

8 _____

_____

_____

*From blossom of the trees
and bushes;
From the roots of the earth
I was made…*

∽

BLODEUEDD'S SONG

9 _____

_____

_____

EARLY CHRISTIAN
SYMBOLS
Book of Kells

10 _____

_____

_____

11 _____

_____

_____

12 _____

_____

_____

13 _____

_____

_____

14 _____

_____

_____

Go shorn and come woolly,
Bear the Beltain female lamb,
be the lovely Bride thee
endowing,
And the fair Mary thee
sustaining,
The fair Mary sustaining thee.

∽

TRADITIONAL MAY BLESSING

Summer has come, healthy
and free,
Whence the brown wood
is bent to the ground
The slender nimble deer leap,
And the path of seals is smooth

The sun smiles over every land –
A parting for me from the brood
of cares:
Hounds bark, stags tryst,
Ravens flourish, summer
has come!

∽

ANON., 10TH CENTURY

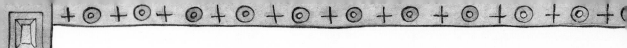

MAY

15 _____

Trees have put on
a beauteous robe.
A mirror is not visible
in the dark.
A candle will not preserve
from cold.
He is not happy who is not
discreet.

~

**THE VIATICUM OF LLEFOED
WYNEBGLAWR**
TRANS. CAITLÍN MATTHEWS

16 *St. Brendan's Day* _____

17 _____

I have come from the Land of
the Living, where there is neither
death nor sin nor transgression.
We enjoy everlasting feasts
without their needing to be
served. We have goodwill
without strife. We live in a great
fairy hill, whence we are called
the People of the Fairy Hills.

~

FROM *THE ADVENTURE OF CONLE*

18 _____

19

20

21

May the sun shine warm
upon your face,
The rain fall soft upon
your fields

TRADITIONAL
IRISH BLESSING

22

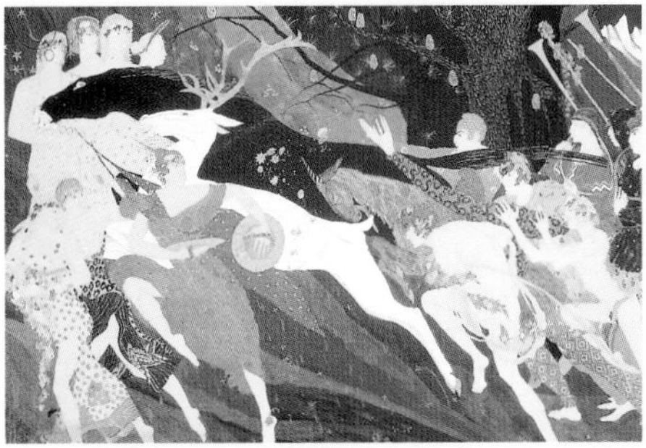

FAIRY PEOPLE
OF THE CELTIC
OTHERWORLD

May

23

24

25

ST. MATTHEW
Book of Kells

26

> I know why there is
> an echo in the hollow;
> Why silver gleams,
> why breath is black . . .
>
> ∽
>
> **FROM *TALIESIN'S SONG***

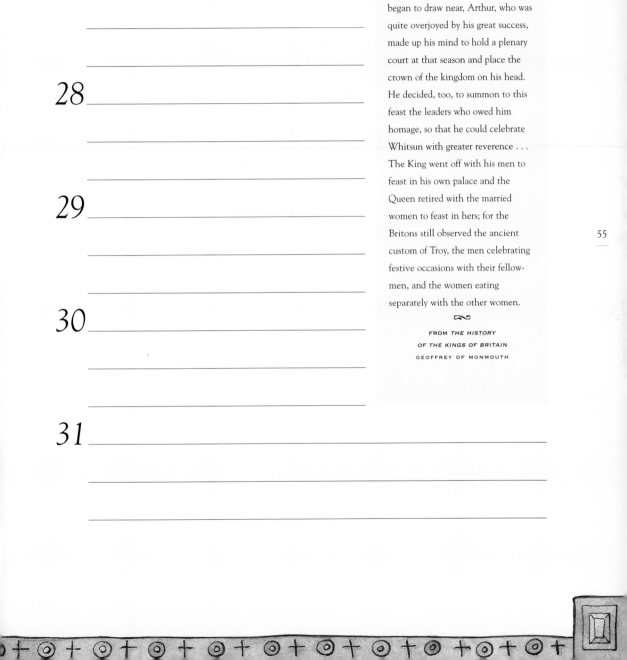

27 _____

_____

_____

28 _____

_____

_____

29 _____

_____

_____

30 _____

_____

_____

31 _____

_____

_____

When the feast of Whitsuntide began to draw near, Arthur, who was quite overjoyed by his great success, made up his mind to hold a plenary court at that season and place the crown of the kingdom on his head. He decided, too, to summon to this feast the leaders who owed him homage, so that he could celebrate Whitsun with greater reverence . . . The King went off with his men to feast in his own palace and the Queen retired with the married women to feast in hers; for the Britons still observed the ancient custom of Troy, the men celebrating festive occasions with their fellow-men, and the women eating separately with the other women.

FROM *THE HISTORY
OF THE KINGS OF BRITAIN*
GEOFFREY OF MONMOUTH

55

June

DRUIDS

THE DRUIDS WERE THE SPIRITUAL LEADERS OF CELTIC society, the wise men to whom everyone deferred in matters of religion, law, and learning. According to Julius Caesar, druids were privileged members of society who were exempt from taxes and military service. They spent about 20 years learning their craft, memorizing the rituals of their religion, all of which was transmitted by word of mouth.

Their name apparently derives from the Greek *drys*, an oak tree, or possibly the Sanskrit *veda*, to know or foresee. The Irish words for wood and wisdom are similar, and druids were gifted people with an immense knowledge of nature. Famously, they made their temples in oak groves where the trees nurtured precious mistletoe.

In many legends they are attributed with the shamanic talent of shape-shifting, changing into animals at will, having power over the weather, and the ability to travel through time.

June

1 _____

_____

_____

"O Cormac, grandson of Conn,"
said Carbery,
"what is the sweetest thing
you have heard?"
"Not hard to tell," said Cormac.
"The shout of triumph
after victory,
praise after wages,
a lady's invitation to her pillow."

2 _____

_____

_____

FROM *THE INSTRUCTIONS*
OF KING CORMAC

3 _____

_____

A good season is summer for
long journeys; quiet is the tall
fine wood, which the whistle of
the wind will not stir; green is
the plumage of the sheltering
wood; eddies swirl in the stream;
good is the warmth of the turf.

FROM *THE FOUR SEASONS*

4 _____

_____

_____

_____

CORMAC RECEIVES
THE CHEERS OF
HIS WARRIORS

5 _____

_____

_____

6 _____

_____

_____

7 _____

_____

. . . the month of June,
when the dew is heaviest . . .

FROM *THE MABINOGION*

_____

June

8

_____

_____

_____

9

_____

_____

_____

THE FIANNA
IN SEARCH OF
THE GIANT

10 _____

_____

_____

11 _____

_____

_____

12 _____

_____

_____

13 _____

_____

_____

14 _____

_____

_____

I am Taliesin.
I sing perfect meter,
Which will last to the end
of the world . . .

I have been a blue salmon,
I have been a dog, a stag, a
roebuck on the mountain,
A stock, a spade, an axe
in the hand,
A stallion, a bull, a buck,
A grain which grew on a hill,
I was reaped and placed
in an oven,
I fell to the ground when
I was being roasted
And a hen swallowed me.
For nine nights was I in her crop.
I have been dead, I am alive,
I am Taliesin.

∾

TALIESIN'S SONG
ANON., 13TH CENTURY

*Advance with determination,
but always fear for the end.*

∾

ST. COLUMBANUS

June

15 _____

_____

_____

16 _____

_____

_____

17 _____

_____

_____

18 _____

_____

_____

62

"If you want to grace the burial place of these men with some lasting monument," replied Merlin, "send for the Giants' Ring which is on Mount Killarus in Ireland . . . These stones are connected with certain secret religious rites, and they have various properties which are medicinally important."

∾

FROM *THE HISTORY OF THE KINGS OF BRITAIN* GEOFFREY OF MONMOUTH

God knows I never saw a better young man for a woman than thou. Hadst thou a woman friend, best of woman's friends wouldst thou be; hadst thou a lady-love, best of lovers wouldst thou be.

∾

FROM *THE LADY OF THE FOUNTAIN*

MERLIN BUILDS
STONEHENGE

19

_____

_____

_____

20

_____

_____

_____

21 Alban Heruin (Light of the Shore) Summer Solstice

_____

_____

I am a shelter for
every poor man, I am a
rampart of fight for every
wealthy man . . .

FROM ***THE***
WOOING OF EMER

June

22

23

24

25

The Druids officiate at the worship of the gods, regulate public and private sacrifices, and give rulings on all religious questions . . . they are held in great honor by the people. They act as judges in practically all disputes, whether between tribes or individuals . . . Any individual or tribe failing to accept their award is banned from taking part in sacrifice – the heaviest punishment that can be inflicted on a Gaul . . . The Druidic doctrine is believed to have been found existing in Britain and thence imported into Gaul; even today those who want to make a profound study of it generally go to Britain for the purpose. The Druids are exempt from military service and do not pay taxes like other citizens.

THE CONQUEST OF GAUL
JULIUS CAESAR

26 _____

_____

_____

27 _____

_____

_____

28 _____

_____

A DRUID AT
THE COURT OF
THE KING

65

29 _____

_____

_____

30 _____

_____

*Three sounds of increase:
the lowing of a cow in milk;
the din of a smithy; the swish
of a plow.*

∽

ANON., TRIAD
9TH CENTURY

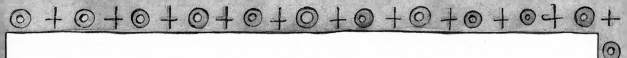

JULY

COURTSHIP

Celtic legend is full of tales of heroes falling in love with beautiful women and of other women abandoning their absent husbands for mightier warriors. While Arthur was fighting in Brittany, for example, Guinevere turned to Mordred for comfort, and many heroines, such as the countess in the tale of the Lady of the Fountain, married their late husband's killers.

For ordinary people, however, marriage was less dramatic, occasionally a matter of love, but more often an arranged match. Trial marriages were entered into at Lughnasadh and lasted until the following Beltain, enabling couples to get to know each other during the long dark winter. Traditionally, if the relationship was unhappy, it was broken off at Beltain, although this was also a season when young lovers came together. Marriages were common after harvest time, since farmers could assess whether they were able to afford a wife.

JULY

1

Length of life and sunny days, and may your souls not go homeward till your own child falls in love!

~

**TRADITIONAL IRISH BLESSING
FOR A BRIDE AND GROOM
TRANS. CAITLÍN MATTHEW**

2

"Leborcham," said Deirdriú, "that man only will I love, who hath three colors that I see yonder – his hair as black as the raven, his cheeks red like blood, and his body as white as the snow."

~

FROM *THE TALE OF DEIRDRIÚ*

3

4

TROUBLED SLEEP

King Arthur
dreams of
fighting the
dragon that is
destroying
Brittany

5 _____

_____

_____

6 _____

_____

_____

7 _____

_____

_____

The hardy,
busy cuckoo calls,
welcome noble summer!

∽

ANON.

JULY

THE CELTIC
OTHERWORLD

*A vision
of paradise*

70

8

9

10 _____

_____

_____

11 _____

_____

_____

12 _____

_____

_____

13 _____

_____

14 _____

_____

_____

Mananan the descendant of
Lir will be
A vigorous bed-fellow to
Caintigern:
He shall be called to his son in
the Beautiful world . . .

He will delight the company
of every fairy-knoll,
He will be the darling of every
godly land,
He will be a dragon before
hosts at the onset,
He will be a wolf of every
great forest . . .

. . . He will be –
his time will be short –
Fifty years in this world:
A dragonstone from the sea
will kill him
In the fight at Senlabor.

∾

THE COMING OF MONGAN
ANON.

_Delightful is the season's
splendor, winter's rough
wind has gone; bright is
the fertile wood, a joyful
peace is summer._

∾

ANON.

15

_____

_____

_____

16

_____

_____

_____

17

_____

_____

_____

18

_____

_____

_____

Be not wise, nor too foolish,
be not too conceited,
nor too diffident,
be not too haughty,
nor too humble,
be not too talkative,
nor too silent,
be not too hard, nor too feeble.

〜

FROM *THE INSTRUCTIONS
OF CORMAC*

Summer brings low the little
stream, the swift herd makes for
the water, the long hair of the
heather spreads out, the weak
white cotton-grass flourishes.

The harp of the wood plays
melody, its music brings perfect
peace; color has settled on
every hill, haze on the lake of
full water.

〜

ANON., 9TH CENTURY

BARDIC
COSTUMES

19 _____

_____

_____

20 _____

_____

_____

21 _____

_____

_____

22 _____

_____

The month of speckled eggs,
of showers of wild garlic,
of delicate roses,
of prosperity . . .

∾

ANON.

JULY

23 _____

_____

_____

24 _____

_____

_____

25 _____

_____

A MOUNTED
SOLDIER

*Silver and gold
plated copper
plaque*

_____

26 _____

*Tomorrow is Lughnasdh Day
when all fruits ripen.*

∾

TRADITIONAL
TRANS. CAITLÍN MATTHEWS

_____

_____

27 _____

_____

_____

28 _____

_____

_____

29 _____

_____

_____

30 _____

_____

31 _____

_____

_____

They continued to feast and
then they began a circuit of
Dyfed; they hunted and enjoyed
themselves, and for roaming the
countryside they had never seen
a more delightful land, nor a
better hunting ground, nor
one better stocked with honey
and fish . . .

∾

FROM *MANAWYDAN, SON OF LIR*
THE MABINOGION

Fair lady, will you travel
To the marvelous land of stars?
Pale as snow the body there,
Under a primrose crown of hair.

∾

ANON., *THE WOOING OF ETAIN*

AUGUST

LUGHNASADH

THE SEASON OF HARVESTS AND THE FINAL QUARTER of the Celtic year begins on 1 August. The druidic festival of Lughnasadh was held in commemoration of the funeral games held by the Irish god Lugh in honor of his foster-mother Tailtiu, the goddess of agriculture. Many regional goddesses were worshiped at the same time.

This was an especially important feast, with celebrations lasting as long as a month. Prophesies stated that as long as the custom was maintained there would be "corn and milk in every house, peace and fine weather for the feast." People who had been surviving on the last remnants of last year's harvest looked forward to this time when food was plentiful and fresh.

Later celebrations may have taken the form of a frenzied circular dance (around a church according to 12th-century chronicler Gerald of Wales). The druids reserved a supply of seed corn for the next year and this was part of the offering to the gods of the harvest.

August

1 *Lughnasadh* _____

_____

_____

2 _____

78

_____

_____

3 _____

_____

_____

4 _____

_____

_____

The Irish, however, began to
kindle a fire under the caldron of
rebirth; corpses were thrown in
until it was full, and next
morning the warriors sprang forth
as fierce as ever, except that they
could not speak.

~

FROM *BRANWEN DAUGHTER OF LIR*
THE MABINOGION.

Wine comes in at the mouth
And love comes in at the eye;
That's all we shall know for truth
Before we grow old and die.
I lift the glass to my mouth,
I look at you and I sigh.

~

A DRINKING SONG
W. B. YEATS

5 _____

_____

6 Cathy's Birthday (1965) _____

_____

_____

7 _____

79

LIFE-GIVING
CALDRON
To revive
fallen warriors

AUGUST

8

_____

_____

_____

*Three glories of a gathering:
a beautiful wife, a good
horse, a swift hound.*

ᔆ

**ANON., TRIAD,
9TH CENTURY**

9

_____

_____

_____

80

THREE HEADS
OF CORMAC

10 _____

_____

_____

11 _____

_____

_____

12 _____

_____

_____

13 _____

_____

_____

14 _____

_____

_____

I was a listener in woods,
I was a gazer at stars,
I was blind where secrets were
concerned,
I was silent in a wilderness,
I was talkative among many,
I was mild in the mead hall,
I was stern in battle,
I was gentle toward allies,
I was a physician to the sick . . .
I did not deride the old though
I was young . . .
I would not speak about anyone
in his absence.

❧

CORMAC MAC AIRT'S BEHAVIOR
AS A CHILD
TRANS. CAITLÍN MATTHEWS

81

August

15 _____

_____

_____

16 _____

_____

_____

17 _____

_____

_____

18 _____

_____

_____

82

Let us not reproach one another,
but rather mutually save
ourselves.
Certain is a meeting after
separation,
The appointment of a senate,
and a certain conference,
And the rising from the grave
after a long repose . . .
To the place where there are
flowers
and dew on pleasant land,
Where there are singers tuning
their harmonious lays.

〜

FROM *THE BLACK BOOK OF
CAERMATHAN*

Since he [King Conaire] assumed
kingship, no cloud has veiled the
sun for the space of a day from
the middle of spring to the
middle of autumn.

〜

FROM *THE TALE OF KING CONAIRE*

ST. CUTHBERT SETS
SAIL TO SPREAD THE
CHRISTIAN GOSPEL

*7th-century
Christian
manuscript*

19 _____

_____

_____

20 _____

_____

_____

21 10 Years Married 2014. _____

_____

_____

22 _____

_____

*The daughter of a king is
a flame of hospitality, a road
that cannot be entered.*

∽

**FROM *THE
WOOING OF EMER***

AUGUST

23 _____

_____

_____

24 _____

_____

25 _____

LANCELOT
AND GUINEVERE

_____

26 _____

_____

_____

27 _____

_____

_____

28 _____

_____

_____

29 _____

_____

_____

30 _____

_____

_____

31 _____

Three rude ones of the world:
a youngster mocking an old man;
a robust person mocking an
invalid; a wise man mocking
a fool.

❧

ANON., TRIAD
9TH CENTURY

Manawydan watched. Toward
midnight he heard the greatest
uproar in the world, and when he
looked there was the largest host
of mice ever – neither number
nor measure could be set upon it.
Before he could move the mice
had fallen upon the croft: each
creature climbed up a stalk of
wheat and, pulling it down,
broke off the ear and carried it
away, leaving the stalk behind,
and as far as he could tell there
was not a single stalk without a
mouse to it.

❧

FROM *MANAWYDAN, SON OF LIR*
THE MABINOGION

*Do not consider
what you are, but what
you will be.*

❧

ST. COLUMBANUS

_____

_____

September

HEROES AND KINGS

THERE ARE A NUMBER OF GREAT CELTIC HEROES: Cú Chulainn of Ulster; Bran, the protector of Britain, who appears in *The Mabinogion*; Pwyll, Prince of Dyfed; and Arthur, the most famous of all legendary kings. Endowed with magical powers and often protected by the gods, they are giants among men (quite literally in Bran's case) and marked from birth for a special purpose. At the time of Arthur's conception, for example, Merlin had magically disguised his father, Uther Pendragon, as his mother's husband Gorlois. Cú Chulainn, the son of the god Lugh, is an invincible hero, destined for a short, but glorious life. Several heroes were bound by *geasa*, or prohibitions, which, if broken, would render them vulnerable or perhaps even kill them. Almost more importantly, their behavior was inextricably bound up with the state of the land: a just king usually produced a prosperous people and a fertile country; a depraved one, famine and ruin.

September

1 _____

_____

_____

2 _____

_____

_____

3 _____

_____

_____

4 _____

_____

_____

Among those feasting men
Cú Chulainn dwelt,
And his young sweetheart close
beside him knelt,
Stared on the mournful wonder
of his eyes,
Even as Spring upon
the ancient skies,
And pondered on the glory
of his days;
And all around the harp-string
told his praise,
And Conchubar, the Red Branch
king of kings,
With his own fingers touched
the brazen strings.

FROM *CÚ CHULAINN'S FIGHT
WITH THE SEA*
W. B. YEATS

CÚ CHULAINN
AND EMER

5

6

7

A good season for staying
is autumn; there is work
then for everyone before
the very short days . . .

ANON., FROM
THE FOUR SEASONS

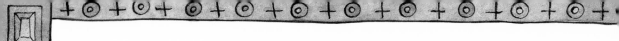

September

8 _____

_____

_____

9 _____

_____

_____

BRANWEN
IMPRISONED IN
THE CASTLE BY
HER HUSBAND

10

11

12

13

14

May the raindrops fall
lightly on your brow
May the soft winds
freshen your spirit
May the sunshine
brighten your heart
May the burden of the day
rest lightly upon you
And may God enfold you in love

OLD IRISH PRAYER

They feasted not in a house
but in tents, for Bran had never
been able to fit inside any house;
they began to carouse, and to
talk, and when they perceived it
was better to sleep than to
continue carousing they went to
bed, and that night Mallolwch
slept with Branwen.

FROM *BRANWEN DAUGHTER OF LIR*
THE MABINOGION

*Three steadiness of good
womanhood: keeping a steady
tongue, a steady chastity,
a steady housewifery.*

ANON., TRIAD,
9TH CENTURY

September

15

16

17

18

If the raven croaks over a closed bed within the house, this denotes that a distinguished guest, whether lay or clerical, is coming to you . . . If it be a layman that is to come, it is bacach! bacach! the raven says . . . If it be a soldier or a satirist that is coming, it is grog! grog! or grob! grob! that it croaks; and it is behind you that the raven speaks and it is from the direction the guests are to come.

∾

EUGENE O'CURREY,
ON THE MANNERS AND CUSTOMS OF THE ANCIENT IRISH, 1873

You shall have mash for your dogs and corn for your horse, and for yourself hot peppered chops and an abundance of wine and entertaining songs.

∾

THE MABINOGION

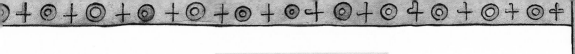

FEDELMA
ATTACKED
BY RAVENS

19 _____

_____

_____

20 _____

_____

21 Alban Elued (Light of the Water) Fall Equinox _____

On Ciarain's feast,
son of the smith
the barnacle goose flies
over cold oceans . . .

THE BOOK OF LEINSTER

_____

_____

September

22 _____

_____

_____

23 _____

_____

_____

24 _____

_____

_____

25 _____

_____

94

If you be too wise,
one will expect too much of you;
if you be too foolish,
you will be deceived;
if you be too conceited,
you will be thought vexatious;
if you be too talkative,
you will not be heeded;
if you be too silent,
you will not be regarded;
if you be too hard,
you will be broken;
if you be too feeble
you will be crushed.

〜

FROM *THE INSTRUCTIONS OF CORMAC*
TRANS. CAITLÍN MATTHEWS

*The whole land, every dale
and glen, weeps its long sorrow
after the graceful summer . . .*

〜

ANON.

26 _____

_____

_____

27 _____

_____

_____

28 _____

_____

_____

29 _____

_____

30 _____

_____

_____

THE LAMENT
OF DEIRDRE

Look before you to the northeast
at the glorious sea, home of
creatures, dwelling of seals,
wanton and splendid, it has
taken on flood tide.

∽

ATTRIB. TO FINAN, 9TH CENTURY

✝ ihs xps · Matheus homo

ongunned   godspeller
incipit euangelii
genelogia mathei
boc

th i
iii
uxant
g i

cynn
necce
nirƺt

LIBER
GENERATI
ONISIHU
XBIFILIIDAUIDFILIIABRAHAM

cnou
nirƺt

ihaelen
dƺ cnirƺes

dauidƺs
runu

abraham
ƺs runu

OCTOBER

CELTIC ART

PRE-CHRISTIAN CELTIC ART WAS FULL OF SYMBOLS and elaborate designs incorporating animals and people, and reflecting their mystical beliefs that everything in the natural world had a magical meaning. It is the work of a society that placed great importance on visual display, and it is clear that even the earliest Celts enameled bronze items to make them more magnificent. Surviving jewelry – torques and brooches – are intricately engraved with linear patterns. The craftsmen did not attempt any kind of narrative on decorated caldrons or shields, but simply used abstract decoration. They were highly skilled and their complex and beautiful work served as status symbols for the leaders of Celtic society. When the hero Cú Chulainn went into battle, for example, his bright clothing and sparkling jewelry were visible signs of his stature. The third-century Roman historian Herodian remarked that: "As they are not used to clothes, they wear iron ornaments about their waists and neck, which they consider to be both decorative and a sign of wealth."

OCTOBER

1

2

3

4

She had a shaggy purple cloak made of fine fleece, and silver brooches of filigree work decorated with handsome gold . . . Wonderful ornamentation of gold and silver with twining animal designs, in the tunic on her breast . . .

FROM *EDAIN THE FAIRY*

Delightful I think it to be in the bosom of an isle, on the peak of a rock, that I might often see there the calm of the sea . . .
That I might see its smooth strand of clear headlands, no gloomy thing; that I might hear the voice of the wondrous birds, a joyful tune.
That I might hear the sound of the shallow waves against the rocks; that I might hear the cry by the graveyard, the noise of the sea.

ANON., 12TH CENTURY

5 _____

_____

_____

*Three locks that unlock
thoughts: drunkenness,
trustfulness, love.*

ANON., TRIAD
9TH CENTURY

6 _____

_____

_____

7 _____

_____

_____

CELTIC WAR
COSTUME

OCTOBER

8 _____

_____

_____

A modest woman is a worm . . . a rush which none comes near.

FROM THE WOOING OF EMER

9 _____

_____

_____

TAPESTRY PAGE
FROM ST. LUKE'S
GOSPEL
*Lindisfarne
Gospels*

10 _____

_____

_____

11 _____

_____

_____

12 _____

_____

13 _____

_____

_____

14 _____

_____

_____

It was with seven faculties that
I was thus blessed,
With seven created beings
I was placed for purification:
I was gleaming fire when
I was caused to exist;
I was dust of the earth,
and grief could not reach me;
I was a high wind,
being less evil than good;
I was a mist on a mountain
seeking supplies of stags;
I was blossoms of trees on
the face of the earth.
If the Lord had blessed me, He
would have placed me on matter.
Soul, such was I made.

∾

*SONG OF THE SOUL
FROM THE BLACK BOOK
OF CARMARTHAN*

OCTOBER

15 _____

_____

_____

16 _____

_____

_____

17 _____

_____

18 _____

_____

_____

I will pick the smooth yarrow that my fingers may be more elegant, that my lips may be warmer, that my voice may be more cheerful. May my voice be like a sunbeam, may my lips be like the juice of the strawberries. May I be an island in the sea, may I be a hill on the land, may I be a star when the moon wanes, may I be a staff to the weak one: I shall wound every man, no man shall wound me.

∾

TRAD. GAELIC FOLK CHARM

19

20

21

22

23

TAPESTRY PAGE
From the
Lindisfarne Gospels

The person who tramples
the world tramples
themselves.

ॐ

ST. COLUMBANUS

October

24 _____

_____

_____

25 _____

_____

_____

26 _____

_____

_____

27 _____

_____

_____

CELTIC WEAPONS

May my fame not perish!
May old age come to me,
may death not come to me
until I am old!

෨

FROM *THE*
SONG OF LONG LIFE

104

28 _____

_____

_____

29 _____

_____

_____

30 _____

_____

_____

31 _____

_____

_____

I am the son of Poetry,
Poetry, son of Reflection,
Reflection, son of Meditation,
Meditation, son of Lore,
Lore, son of Research,
Research, son of Great
Knowledge,
Great Knowledge,
son of Intelligence,
Intelligence,
son of Comprehension,
Comprehension, son of Wisdom,
Wisdom son of the three gods
of Dana.

∽

THE COLLOQUY OF THE TWO SAGES

O man that diggest the tomb,
And that puttest my darling
from me,
Make not the grave too narrow,
I shall be beside the noble ones.

∽

DEIRDRIÚ'S LAMENT

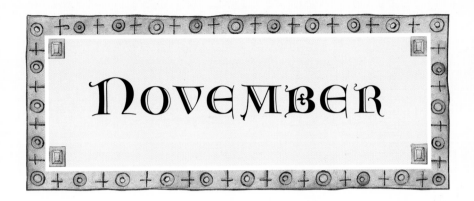

November

SAMHAIN

Samhain, THE FESTIVAL THAT MARKED THE BEGINNING of winter, was the greatest in the Celtic calendar, and signified the new year. The bonfires which we still associate with this time of year may have had their origins in the ancient habit of slaughtering cattle unfit for overwintering and burning their carcasses. More importantly, feasting helped to ward off the gloom of the long winter nights. Rather like the beliefs and traditions surrounding Halloween, Samhain was associated with communion between the living and the dead, when the gates of the Otherworld were opened to allow spirits to walk the earth.

The Celts believed that the mighty goddess Cailleach struck the ground with her hammer, making the earth iron-hard until Imbolc, three months later. The Irish legend of Cú Chulainn states that the Samhain celebrations lasted for a week, and other tales feature sacrifices to appease the gods.

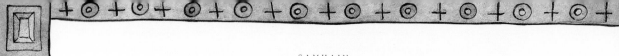

November

1 *Samhain*

2

3

4

Every year the men of Ulster were accustomed to hold festival together; and the time when they held it was for three days before Samhain, and for three days after that day, and upon Samhain itself . . . nor was there anything in the world that they would do that time except sports and marketings, and splendors, and pomps, and feasting and eating . . .

FROM *THE WASTING SICKNESS OF CÚ CHULAINN*

The Calends of Winter,
the time of pleasant gossiping,
The gale and the storm
keep equal pace;

RED BOOK OF HERGEST
TRANS. CAITLÍN MATTHEWS

THE MEN
OF ULSTER

5 _____

_____

_____

6 _____

_____

Three sources of new life;
a woman's belly, a hen's egg,
a wrong forgiven.

༄

ANON., TRIAD,
9TH CENTURY

7 _____

_____

_____

November

DOLMEN
STONE

110

8

9

*Three things that are always ready
in a decent man's house: beer, a
bath, a good fire.*

**ANON., TRIAD,
9TH CENTURY**

10 _____

_____

_____

11 _____

_____

_____

12 _____

_____

_____

13 _____

_____

_____

14 _____

_____

_____

I invoke the seven daughters
of the sea
Who fashion the threads of the
sons of long life.
May three deaths be taken
from me!
May seven waves of good fortune
be dealt to me!
May no evil spirits harm me
on my circuit!

. . . I am not an indestructible
stronghold.
I am an unshaken rock.
I am a precious stone.
I am the luck of the week.
May I live a hundred times a
hundred years.
Each hundred of them apart!

∽

FROM *THE SONG OF LONG LIFE*
ANON., 5TH CENTURY

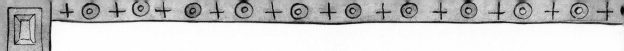

November

15 _____

_____

_____

B̲e simple in faith but well
trained in manners; demanding
in your own affairs, but
unconcerned in those of others . . .

~

ST. COLUMBANUS

16 _____

_____

_____

I̲ have news for you;
the stag bells, winter snows,
summer has gone.
Wind high and cold,
the sun low, short its course,
the sea running high.
Deep red the bracken,
its shape lost; the wild goose has
raised its accustomed cry.
Cold has seized the bird's wings;
the season of ice, this is my news.

~

THE COMING OF WINTER
ANON., IRISH, 9TH CENTURY

17 _____

_____

_____

18 _____

_____

_____

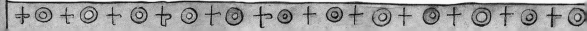

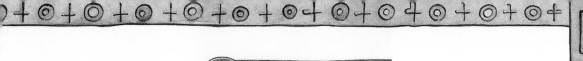

ST. MATTHEW'S
GOSPEL

From the
Stockholm Codex
(8th century)

19 _____

_____

_____

20 _____

_____

_____

21 _____

Three deaths that are
better than life: the death of
a salmon, the death of a fat pig,
the death of a thief.

ᕗ

ANON., TRIAD, 9TH CENTURY
TRANS. CAITLÍN MATTHEWS

_____

_____

November

22
_____

_____

_____

23
_____

_____

_____

114

24
_____

_____

_____

25
_____

_____

_____

Bid that a strong ghost
stand at the head
That my Michael may
sleep sound,
Nor cry, not turn in the bed
Till his morning meal
come round;
And may departing twilight keep
All dread afar till morning's back,
That his mother may not lack
Her fill of sleep.

❧

A PRAYER FOR MY SON
W. B. YEATS

May the road rise to meet you,
May the wind be always
at your back

❧

TRADITIONAL
IRISH BLESSING

26 _____

_____

27 _____

_____

_____

28 _____

_____

_____

29 _____

_____

_____

30 _____

_____

_____

ST. COLUMBA

In Conaire's reign are the three
crowns on Erin, namely, a crown
of corn ears, and a crown of
flowers, and a crown of oak mast
. . . each man deems the other's
voice as melodious as the strings
of harps, because of the
excellence of the law and the
peace and the goodwill
prevailing throughout Erin.

THE TALE OF KING CONAIRE

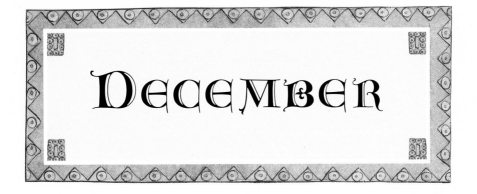

December

SAINTS

THE CELTIC TALENT FOR STORY-TELLING TRANSFERRED easily to the wonderful and miraculous lives of the Christian saints. The Irish were among the earliest people to be converted by Roman missionaries, but with the fall of the Roman empire, Irish Christianity was abandoned by Rome for about 200 years and was not fully assimilated again until the 12th century.

Saints Patrick, Columba, David, and Brendan, to name a few, survive in legends as vivid as those about their pagan forebears. They were endowed with qualities similar to those of bards and druids, and they respected animals and the natural order. Many shared a devout asceticism – St. Brendan, for example, would not sully his ears with the pleasure of hearing music and kept two pieces of wax on a long string with him at all times, in case he should inadvertently fall prey to a tune.

December

1 _____

_____

_____

2 _____

118

_____

_____

3 _____

_____

_____

4 _____

_____

_____

Their musical instruments charm
and delight the ear with their
sweetness . . . In their rhymed
songs and set speeches they are so
subtle and ingenious that they
produce, in their native tongue,
ornaments of wonderful and
exquisite invention both in
words and sentences. Hence arise
those poets whom they call
Bards, of whom you will find
many in this nation . . .

GERALD OF WALES

There is a caldron
of invigorating mead,
For the use of the inmates
of the house.
It never grows less; it is a custom
That it should be full for ever.

FROM *THE WASTING
SICKNESS OF CÚ CHULAINN*

TALES TOLD
BY THE BARD

5 _____

_____

_____

6 _____

_____

_____

7 _____

*I know why . . . a cow
has horns; why a woman
is affectionate . . .*

∽

FROM *TALIESIN'S SONG*

_____

_____

December

8 _____

. _____

_____

*Three false sisters: "Perhaps,"
"Maybe," "I dare say."*

〜

ANON., TRIAD
9TH CENTURY

9 _____

_____

_____

ST. DAVID

10 _____

_____

_____

11 _____

_____

_____

12 _____

I arise today
Through the strength of heaven:
Light of sun,
Radiance of moon,
Splendor of Fire,
Speed of Lightning,
Swiftness of wind,
Depth of sea,
Stability of earth,
Firmness of rock.

ATTRIB. ST. PATRICK
TRANS. CAITLÍN MATTHEWS

_____

13 _____

_____

In the black season of deep
winter a storm of waves is roused
along the expanse of the world . . .
the iron pot is put on the fire
after the dark black day . . .

FROM *THE FOUR SEASONS*

14 _____

_____

_____

December

15 _____

_____

_____

16 _____

_____

_____

17 _____

_____

_____

18 _____

_____

_____

122

Arthur was a young man only fifteen years old; but he was of such outstanding courage and generosity, and his inborn goodness gave him such grace that he was loved by almost all the people.

∽

FROM *THE HISTORY OF THE KINGS OF BRITAIN* GEOFFREY OF MONMOUTH [TRADITIONALLY, KING ARTHUR'S BIRTHDAY WAS CELEBRATED ON 21 DECEMBER]

All the Britons dye their bodies with woad, which produces a blue color, and this gives them a more terrifying appearance in battle. They wear their hair long and shave the whole of their bodies except the head and the upper lip.

∽

THE CONQUEST OF GAUL JULIUS CAESAR

19 <u>My birthday (1960)</u>

20

21

22 Alban Arthuan (Light of Arthur) Winter Solstice. Traditionally King Arthur's Birthday

*They are beautiful women,
victorious, never knowing the
sorrow of the vanquished.*

~

**FROM *THE WASTING*
*SICKNESS OF CÚ CHULAINN***

123

December

23 _____

Three things that constitute
a physician: a complete cure;
leaving no blemish behind;
a painless examination.

ANON., TRIAD, 9TH CENTURY

24 _____

25 _____

26 _____

*Always be sober,
chaste, modest.*

ST. COLUMBANUS

27 _____

_____

28 _____

_____

29 _____

_____

30 _____

_____

_____

31 _____

_____

_____

OLWEN

Olwen came, dressed in a flame-
red silk robe, with a torque of red
gold round her neck, studded
with precious pearls and rubies.
Her hair was yellower than
broom, her skin whiter than sea
foam, her palms and fingers were
whiter than shoots of marsh
trefoil against the sand of a
welling spring . . . anyone who
saw her would fall deeply in love.

FROM *HOW CULWECH WON OLWEN*
THE MABINOGION

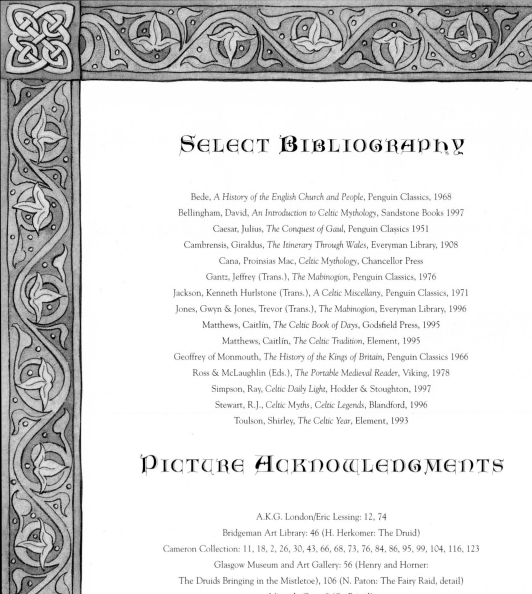

Select Bibliography

Bede, *A History of the English Church and People*, Penguin Classics, 1968

Bellingham, David, *An Introduction to Celtic Mythology*, Sandstone Books 1997

Caesar, Julius, *The Conquest of Gaul*, Penguin Classics 1951

Cambrensis, Giraldus, *The Itinerary Through Wales*, Everyman Library, 1908

Cana, Proinsias Mac, *Celtic Mythology*, Chancellor Press

Gantz, Jeffrey (Trans.), *The Mabinogion*, Penguin Classics, 1976

Jackson, Kenneth Hurlstone (Trans.), *A Celtic Miscellany*, Penguin Classics, 1971

Jones, Gwyn & Jones, Trevor (Trans.), *The Mabinogion*, Everyman Library, 1996

Matthews, Caitlín, *The Celtic Book of Days*, Godsfield Press, 1995

Matthews, Caitlín, *The Celtic Tradition*, Element, 1995

Geoffrey of Monmouth, *The History of the Kings of Britain*, Penguin Classics 1966

Ross & McLaughlin (Eds.), *The Portable Medieval Reader*, Viking, 1978

Simpson, Ray, *Celtic Daily Light*, Hodder & Stoughton, 1997

Stewart, R.J., *Celtic Myths, Celtic Legends*, Blandford, 1996

Toulson, Shirley, *The Celtic Year*, Element, 1993

Picture Acknowledgments

A.K.G. London/Eric Lessing: 12, 74

Bridgeman Art Library: 46 (H. Herkomer: The Druid)

Cameron Collection: 11, 18, 2, 26, 30, 43, 66, 68, 73, 76, 84, 86, 95, 99, 104, 116, 123

Glasgow Museum and Art Gallery: 56 (Henry and Horner:
The Druids Bringing in the Mistletoe), 106 (N. Paton: The Fairy Raid, detail)

Miranda Gray: 8 (St. Brigid)

Alan Lee: 90, 125

Paisley Museum and Art Gallery: 53 (O. Carleton Smyth: Fairy Rout (Bacchanale))

The Stock Market: 15, 110